THE MACMILLAN READING PROGRAM

Senior Authors
Albert J. Harris
Mae Knight Clark

LANDS OF PLEASURE

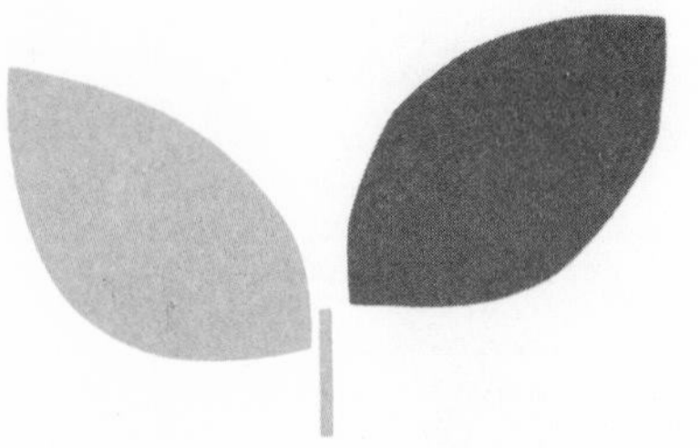

Books are keys to wisdom's treasure;
Books are gates to lands of pleasure;
Books are paths that upward lead;
Books are friends. Come let us read.

"Books Are Keys," *by Emilie Poulsson*

Mae Knight Clark

LANDS OF PLEASURE

THE MACMILLAN COMPANY, NEW YORK
COLLIER-MACMILLAN LIMITED, LONDON

The Macmillan Company, New York
Collier-Macmillan Canada, Ltd., Toronto, Ontario
Printed in the United States of America

Illustrated by

John Falter, Symeon Shimin, Ed Young,
George Porter, Tom Vroman

Grateful acknowledgment is made to the following authors
and publishers for permission to use copyrighted material:

Abelard-Schuman Limited, for "Jack and Jim," an adaptation of *Jack and Jim* by Esphyr Slobodkina, by permission of Abelard-Schuman Limited, all rights reserved; for "Shooting Stars" from the book *Runny Days, Sunny Days* by Aileen Fisher, by permission of Abelard-Schuman Limited, all rights reserved, copyright year 1958.

Child Life, for "Patches," an adaptation of "Patches" by Margarita Parry, from *Child Life Magazine*, copyright 1950 by Child Life.

Doubleday & Company, Inc., for "Tommy and Ben," text and illustrations adapted from *The Little Twin* by Grace Paull, copyright 1953 by Grace Paull, reprinted by permission of Doubleday & Company, Inc.

E. P. Dutton & Company, Inc., for "Horsemanship" copyright 1941 by Marchette Chute, from the book *Around and About* by Marchette Chute, published 1957 by E. P. Dutton & Company, Inc., and reprinted with their permission.

Harcourt, Brace & World, Inc., for "Teddy and Babs," adapted from *Two and Two Are Four* by Carolyn Haywood, copyright 1940 by Harcourt, Brace & World, Inc., and reprinted with permission of the publishers; for "What's the Funniest Thing?" excerpted from the poem "What's the Funniest Thing?" © 1958 by Beatrice Schenk de Regniers, from the volume *Something Special* reprinted by permission of Harcourt, Brace & World, Inc.

Harper & Row, Inc., for "My Zipper Suit" from *A Pocketful of Poems* by Marie Louise Allen, copyright © 1957 by Marie Allen Howarth.

Holiday House, Inc., for "Lucy," an adaptation of "Who is Terry?" from *The Birthday Story* by Ruth Jaeger Buntain, through a special arrangement with Holiday House, Inc.

Lothrop, Lee and Shepard Co., Inc., for "Books are Keys" by Emilie Poulsson, by permission of Lothrop, Lee and Shepard Co., Inc.

William Morrow and Company, Inc., for "On Green Street," an adaptation of a chapter from *Betsy's Busy Summer* by Carolyn Haywood, copyright © 1956 by The Curtis Publishing Company, copyright © 1956 by Carolyn Haywood, by permission of William Morrow and Company, Inc.

William R. Scott, Inc., for "The High Jump," adapted from *The Little Rabbit, The High Jumper* by Miriam Schlein, copyright 1957 by Miriam Schlein, permission granted by the publisher, William R. Scott, Inc.

Contents

Children to Know

Friends on the Farm

Fun with Make-Believe

Rockets Away!

Children to Know

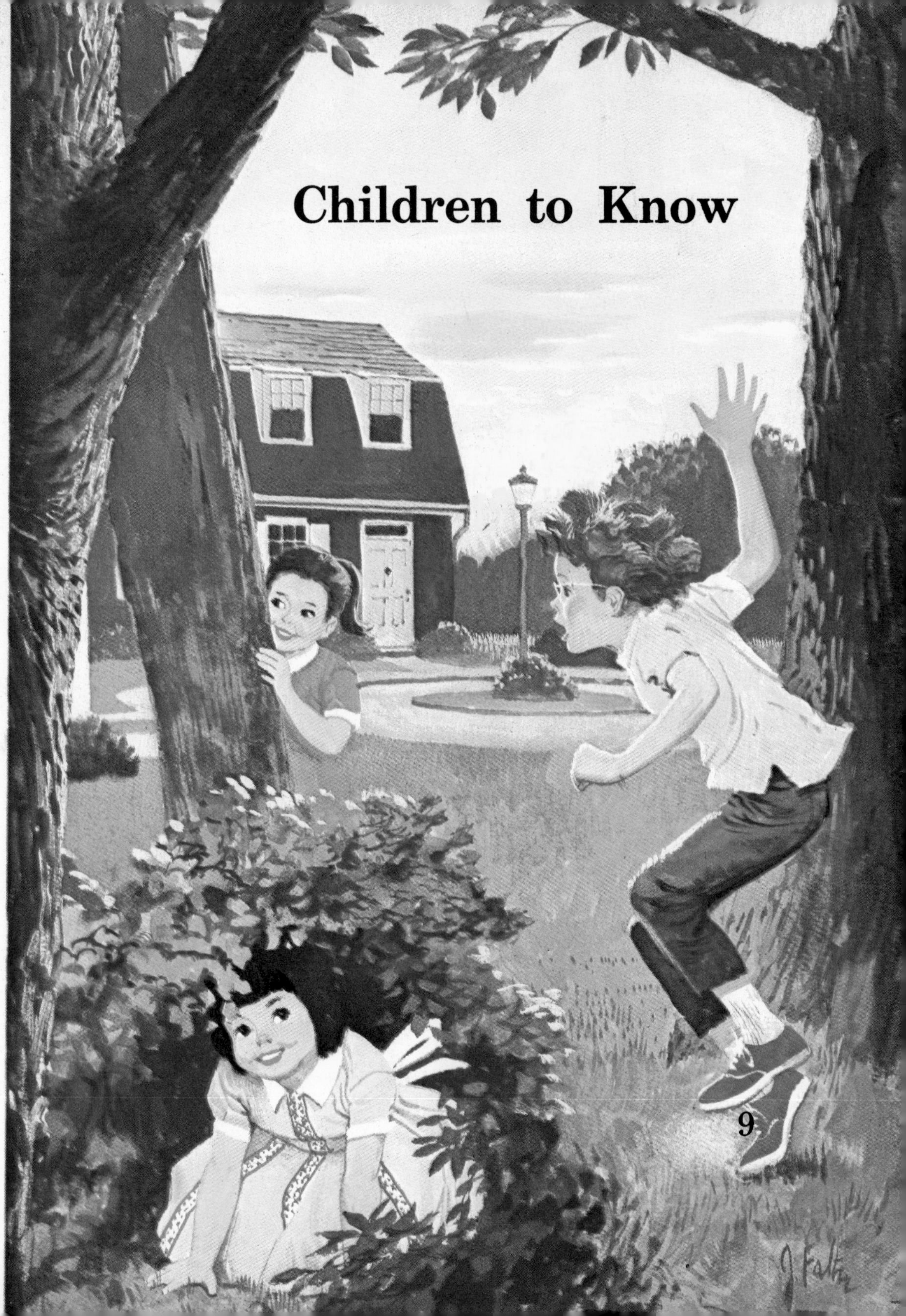

On Green Street

Green Street is a little street.
It runs up and down and around.
It has trees and houses on it.

Birds live in the trees on Green Street.

Children live in all but one of the houses.

The children like to live on Green Street.

Betsy is one of the children
who live on Green Street.

Betsy has a little sister.

The little sister is Star.

Betsy and Star live
in the big brown house.

Something for the Children

One day Betsy said,
"Please, Daddy! Make us a pool."

"What do you want with a pool?"
asked Betsy's father.

"I just like a pool," said Betsy.
"I want to put fish in it.
I want to play with boats in it."

"Oh, I want a pool, too!" said Star.
"Please make us a pool, Daddy.
Just a little one, please!"

So Betsy's father did make a pool for Betsy and Star.

It was a little pool.

It was just right for little fish.

Star said, "Oh, Daddy!

The fish will like to live in that pool."

All the children on Green Street went to see the fish.

It was fun to play with boats in the pool, too.

Then Betsy's father said,
"I know what I will do.
I will make a little house for you.
I will paint it white.
You and Star can help me paint it."

It was fun to help paint the house.
Betsy and Star liked to play in it.
All the children on Green Street
liked to play in it, too.
The little house looked like
a big white bird cage.

The mothers on Green Street liked the little house, too.

They asked, "Why don't you go play with Betsy and her sister?

Go play in the little house.

You like the big bird cage."

That is just what the children did.

At Betsy's House

One day Ellen went to play with Betsy.

Ellen's little sister Linda went, too.

Betsy was in the little house.

Ellen said, "Let's play we live here in the little white house."

"All right," said Betsy.

"You and I will play house.

Linda, why don't you go play with Star?"

Star said, "Come on, Linda.
I know what we can do.
I will put on a dress of Mother's.
You can put one on, too.
We will play dress up."

"Oh, good!" said Linda.
She liked to play dress up.

Star put on a dress
of her mother's.
It was a white dress.
Linda put on a black one.

Then they went out to play.
"Call Betsy," said Linda.
"Tell her to look at us.
I want her to see my black dress."

Just then Linda fell down.

Star began to call for help.
"Betsy!" she called.
"Linda is in the pool.
Come help me get her out!"

Linda was wet.
Her black dress was wet, too.
She began to cry.

Betsy and Ellen ran out
of the little white house.

"Oh, look!" said Ellen.
"Linda is in the pool.
We must get her out!"

Ellen and Betsy tried
to get Linda out.
Linda didn't help at all.

"Don't cry," said Ellen.
"Don't cry, Linda.
Did you get hurt?"

"I don't know," said Linda.

"Then why do you cry?"
asked Betsy.
"We will get you out."

"Did Linda hurt the fish?"
asked Star.
"I don't want the fish hurt."

Linda Gets Out

Ellen said, "Oh, Linda,
you are so wet!
You must get out.
I will help you."

"No!" said Linda.
"I can't get out."

"Here!" said Betsy.
"We will get you out."

"No! No!" said Linda.
"You will hurt me!"

Star was down by the pool.
She wanted to see about the fish.

She said, "Count the fish, Betsy.
See if Linda hurt the fish."

"You can count," said Betsy.
"You are not a baby.
Why don't you count the fish?
I must get Linda out of the pool."

So Star began to count the fish.

She said, "One, two, three, four, five, six.

That's right.

Six fish live in the pool."

Then she said, "Linda didn't hurt the fish.

All six fish are here."

"That's good," said Ellen.

"Yes, it is good," said Star.

Star liked the fish.

Betsy said, "Here, Linda,
you can get out with this.
We will help you."

"Don't help me!" said Linda.
"I can do it!
I can do it!"

"All right!" said Ellen,
and she let go of Linda.
Betsy let go of her, too.
Linda fell back again,
but she didn't cry.

"I like it here," said Linda.
"I like this pool.
I won't get out of it."

"This pool is not for you,"
said Star.
"It is for the fish."

Ellen said,
"You come out of that pool, Linda!
Right now!
If you don't, you can't come back
to play here again!"

Linda got right out of the pool!

What About the Fish?

Star got down by the pool again to count the fish.

"One, two, three, four, five," she said.

"Just five!
Six fish live in the pool.
All the fish are not here."

Then she began to yell,
"One is not here!
Betsy! One fish is not here!"

"You didn't count right,"
said Betsy.
"Count again."

Star began to count again,
"One, two, three, four, five.
Just five are here, Betsy!"

Betsy got down by the pool
to count the fish.
"I don't see the yellow one
with black on it," said Betsy.

"No," said Star.
"I don't see that one."

Ellen said, "You are so wet, Linda.
Let me help you take off
this wet dress."

She got the wet black dress
off Linda.

Just then Linda began
to jump up and down and yell.
"Oh!" she yelled.
"Get it out! Get it out!"

Betsy and Star jumped up.

"What is it?" asked Ellen.
"Why are you yelling so?"

"Something is in here!"
yelled Linda.
"Something is in here!"

"Don't jump around and yell
like that," said Ellen.
"I will get it out."

"The fish!" said Betsy.
"I just know it is the fish."

It **was** the fish from the pool!
Linda didn't stop
jumping up and down and yelling.
But Ellen got the fish out.

"It **is** the fish!" yelled Ellen.
"Here it is!"

"Stop yelling and give it to me," said Betsy.

They all got down by the pool.
Betsy put the little fish back.

"Oh!" said Star.
"The little fish is all right."

"All of the fish are all right," said Ellen.
"They were not hurt."

Just then Betsy saw her mother.

"Oh, Mother," she yelled.
"Ellen's little sister
got wet in the pool."

Mother looked at Linda.
"I see that she did," said Mother.
"Is she hurt?"

"No, Mother," said Star.
"A fish got out of the pool with her.
We put it back.
It was the black and yellow fish."

Mother got down by Linda.
She said, "Why, Linda,
you are so wet!
Come with me.
I will give you a dress to put on.
I will give you one
that is not too big or too little.
One that is not wet."

Jack and Jim

Jack and Jim were two boys on Green Street.

The boys' house was right by Betsy's house.

It was white.

Jack and Jim were brothers.
Jack looked just like Jim.
Jim looked just like Jack.
They were twin brothers.

Jack liked to do what Jim did.
Jim liked to do what Jack did.
They liked to play together.

Jack liked all the children on Green Street.
But he liked his twin brother best of all.
Jim liked all the children on Green Street, too.
But he liked his twin brother best of all.

From Morning to Night

In the morning the boys said, "Hello, Jack."

"Hello, Jim."

This is how the twins began a good day together.

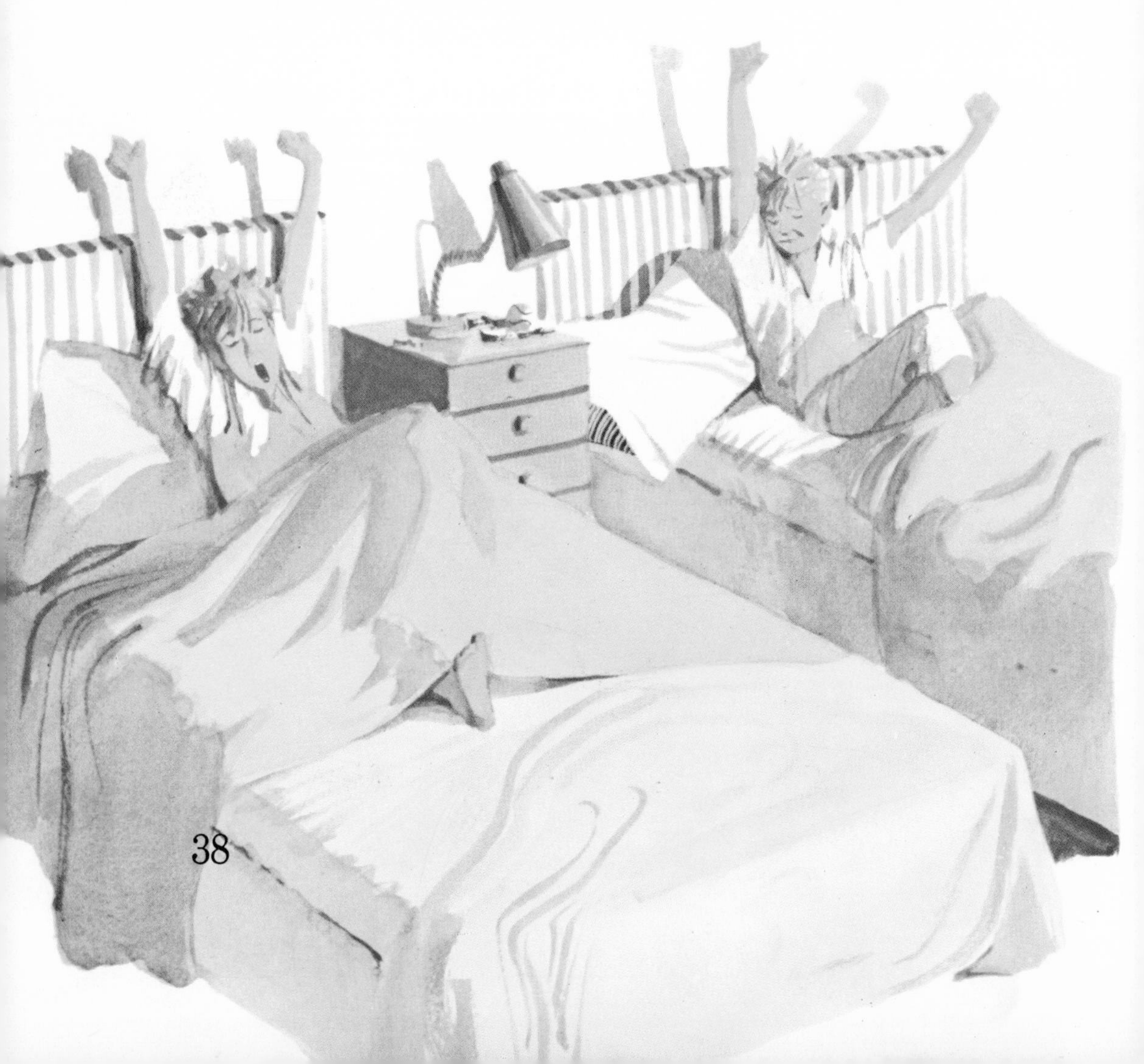

At night the twins said,
"Good night, Jack."
"Good night, Jim."

Then they went to sleep.

One day Jack said, "If you go away, I will write to you, Jim. I will write you a letter."

Jim laughed.
He said, "That's good, Jack.
But you won't write the letter.
If I go away, you will go, too."

Jack laughed.
"That's right," he said.
"If you go, I will go, too."

Jim said, "You are
the best brother a boy ever had."

"No," said Jack.
"You are the best brother
a boy ever had."

The boys laughed.
They liked to live together.
They wanted to eat together
and play together and sleep together.

A Show on TV

Jack and Jim liked to look at TV.
They looked at one TV show
in the morning.
They looked at one show at night.

One day the twins were looking
at a TV show.
They saw a man on it.
The man had a little dog.

The man said,
"We will give this dog away.
I will tell you
how you may get him.
Just write a letter to me.
Tell me why you want
the little dog.
The one who writes the best letter
will get the puppy.
Why not try it?
You may get the dog!"

The twins looked
at the little dog on the TV.

He was the cutest little puppy
they had ever seen!

What the Twins Do

The TV show was over.
Jack looked at Jim.
Jim looked at Jack.
They said together,
"I want that little puppy!"
It was fun just to talk
about the puppy.

"I love that puppy," said Jack.
"I know I can take care of him."

"I love that puppy," said Jim.
"I know I can take care of him."

"Why not write a letter?" said Jim.
"Let's try to get that puppy."

"Can we do it?" asked Jack.

"I don't know, but we can try,"
said Jim.

All that day they tried
to write the letter.
That letter was hard to write.
The next morning and the next night
they tried again.
On the next day after that
they did write it!

The Letter

We are twin brothers, Jack and Jim.
If we get the little puppy,
We will take good care of him.
Two of us will love him,
And not just one.
Two will play ball with him
And see that he has fun.
For that little puppy
On the TV screen
Was the cutest little puppy
We have ever seen.

Jim Jones
Jack Jones

After the letter went,
the twins looked and looked at TV.

They didn't see the little dog.

Then one morning they were
looking at TV again.

They saw the man
who had the dog.

The man said, "Now we can tell you
who had the best letter.

It was hard to tell the best one.

So we won't give just one prize.

We will give three."

Then the TV man showed
one of the prizes.

He said, "This is not
the first prize.

It **is** something you will like.

A boy gets this prize.

I will tell you his name."

The man didn't say, "Jack Jones."

He didn't say, "Jim Jones."

He didn't say the name
of a boy or girl on Green Street.

The twins didn't get that prize.

The TV man showed a cat for the next prize.

He said the name of the one who was to get the cat.

He didn't say, "Jack Jones."
He didn't say, "Jim Jones."
He said the name of a girl.

"I don't care if she did get the cat," said Jim.
"That's not the prize I want."

"No," said Jack.
"It is not the prize I want."

"Now comes the puppy,"
said the TV man.
He showed the little brown puppy.

"The puppy is the first prize,"
he said.
"It is the cutest little puppy
we have ever seen."

Jack and Jim were looking
at the TV.

The man said,
"This prize will go to twin boys.

They live on Green Street.

Their names are
Jack and Jim Jones."

Jack and Jim jumped up and down.

They yelled to their mother
about the prize puppy.

Their mother said, "Good!

You will love the little puppy.

Now do stop yelling so!"

Two days went by.
Then they got the puppy.

"He is the cutest puppy
I have ever seen!" said Jack.

Jim said, "He is
the cutest puppy I have ever seen!"

"You must try to take good care
of him," said their mother.

"Oh, we will!" said the twins.
"We will love him, too."

The twins wanted to show
the puppy to the children.
So they went out
on Green Street with him.

Jack and Jim ran with the puppy.
He jumped around and played.
It was hard to run with him.
All the girls and boys
on Green Street liked the puppy.

The twins went back to their house.
The puppy had something to eat.
Then he went to sleep.

The Puppy's Name

The twins were looking
at the puppy.

"I just love that puppy!" said Jack.

"I love him, too," said Jim.

Then Jack looked at Jim.
Jim looked at Jack.
The boys said together,
"The puppy has no name!"

"We must name him," said Jack.

"Yes," said Jim.
"We must give him a name.
What can we name him?"

Jack said a name that he liked.
"No," said Jim.
"I don't like that name."

Then Jim said a name
that he liked.
"No," said Jack.
"I don't like that name."

Jim tried again.
Jack didn't like that name.

Jack said three or four names.
Jim said three or four names.
Jim didn't want the names
Jack wanted.
Jack didn't want the names
Jim wanted.

So it went.
The boys began to quarrel.

The name Jack liked best was Zip.
The name Jim liked best
was Snapper.

Jim didn't like Zip.
Jack didn't like Snapper.

Jack said, "He must have a name.
We will call the puppy Zip."

"No, we won't call him Zip,"
said Jim.
"His name is Snapper."

"I don't care what you say,"
said Jack.
"His name is not Snapper!
I won't have it!"

That night Jack didn't say
good night to Jim.

Jim didn't say
good night to Jack.

That was the first night
that the boys had not said good night.

It was hard not to say good night.

But they didn't say it.

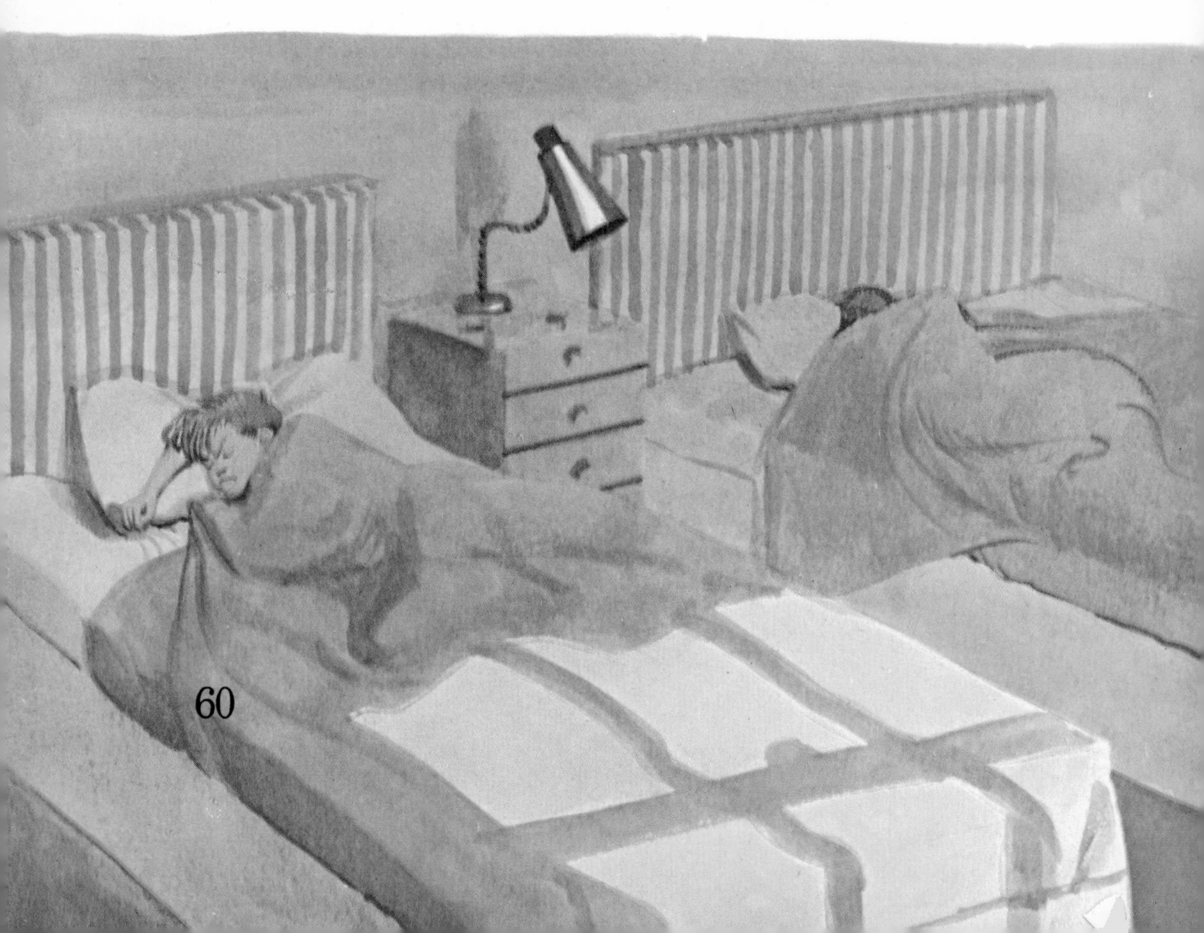

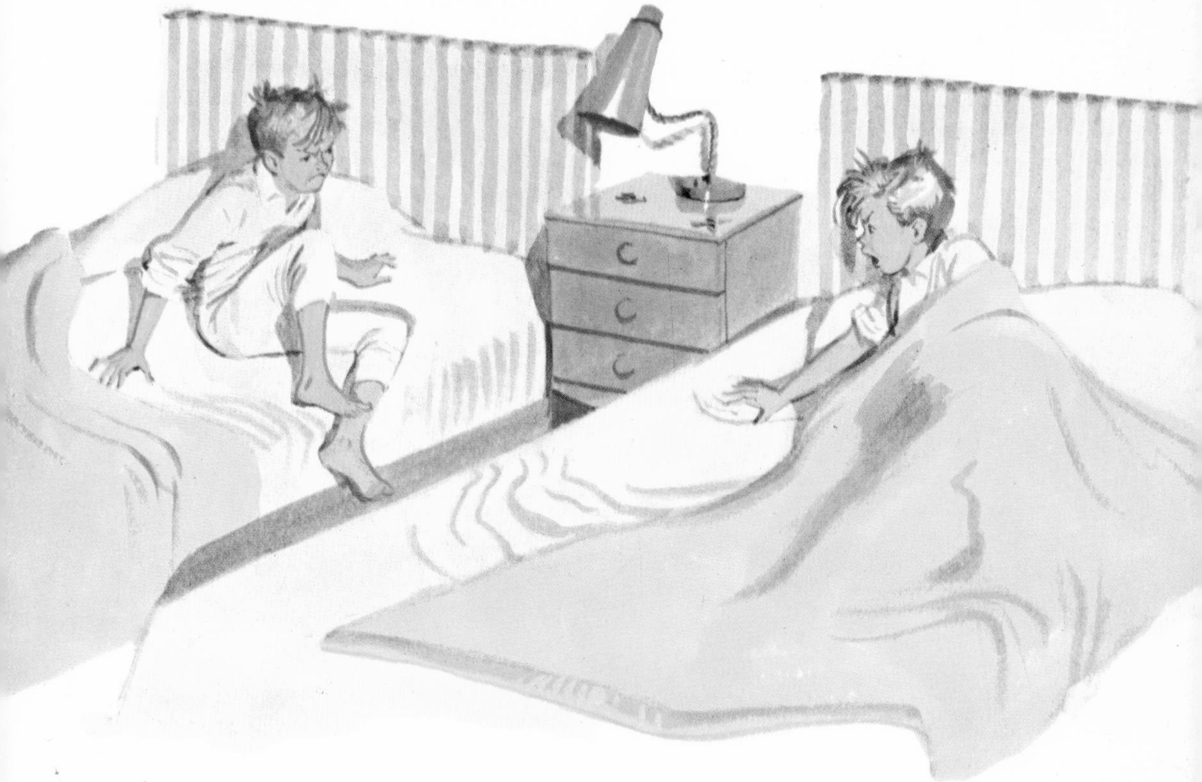

The next morning came,
and the boys got up.

Jack didn't say good morning
to Jim.

Jim didn't say good morning
to Jack.

They just began to quarrel again
about the puppy's name.

Day after day went by.
The boys didn't name the puppy.
The twins' father said,
"This puppy must have a name.
Why don't you boys
get together about it?"

It was hard for the twins
to get together on a name.
All they did was quarrel.

No Puppy!

One day the twins came in
and didn't see the little dog.

They looked all around
in the house.

They went out and looked
up and down the street.

They didn't see the little dog.

Their puppy was lost.

The boys wanted to call the puppy.

How could they call him
if he had no name?

All the boys could do
was whistle for their lost dog.
At the first whistle,
a little dog came on the run.
He was not their dog.

At the next whistle, a big dog came.
A little black dog came, too.
Their puppy didn't come.

At the next whistle,
five or six dogs came.
Big dogs and little dogs came.
Not one of the dogs
was their little brown puppy.

All that day the twins
looked for their prize puppy.

They asked the boys and girls
on Green Street about him.

No one had seen
the little dog go by.

Night came, and the boys
had to stop looking.

It was hard to go back
with no puppy.

Both of the twins wanted to cry,
but they didn't.

That night the puppy came back to their house.

He wanted something to eat.

The twins were so happy!

They were too happy to quarrel.

The puppy was happy, too.

The boys got the puppy something to eat.

Then it went to sleep.

Good Friends Again

The twins were both looking
at the puppy.
Then they began to quarrel again.

"You don't try to name him,"
said Jack.
"Zip is the right name for him."

"You are the one," said Jim.
"You won't try to name him!
The right name is Snapper."

The twins' father said, "Now, boys.
Don't quarrel like that.
It won't help."

"But Daddy!" said Jim.
"If the puppy had a name,
we could call him.
Jack won't let him
have a name.
Jack won't call the puppy Snapper."

Jack said, "No, Daddy!
It is Jim who won't let him
have a name.
He won't call the puppy Zip."

"Both of you can't have
what you want," said their father.
"Both of you must give in a little.
You must get together on a name."

"How?" asked Jack.

"How?" asked Jim.

"I can tell you something to try," said Mr. Jones.

"First write the two names you like best.

Then I will show you."

The boys did that.

"Now!" said Mr. Jones.

"Write the first three letters of the name Jack likes."

The boys counted the letters.

"Zip!" said both boys together.

"Now write the last three letters of the name Jim likes."

"Per!" said Jack and Jim.

"Now put the two together," said their father.

"What do you get?"

"Zipper!" yelled both boys.

Now if you go on Green Street, you may see two little boys.

Both of the boys may call together, "Zipper! Zipper!"

Down the street will run a little brown puppy.

It will be the cutest little puppy you have ever seen.

You will see two happy boys. They are good brothers again. They are good friends, too.

Lucy

A little girl came to live
in a new house on Green Street.
Her name was Lucy.
She had no brothers or sisters.
She had no pets.

At their last house
Lucy had friends to play with her.
They lived all around her.
But she didn't know the children
on Green Street.

Lucy had seen the boys and girls
who lived on Green Street.
She knew their names,
but they didn't know her.

Day after day she saw
the children playing together.
She wanted to play, too,
but they didn't call her to come over.

One day something was not right
with the wheels on Betsy's bike.
Lucy wanted to say, "Ride my bike."
But she didn't.

One morning Lucy went down the street.

She had on a new dress.

It was red and black, and it was her best dress.

Lucy wanted to show the new dress to a friend.

But she had no friends on Green Street.

Lucy came to the last house on the street.

She saw a blue package.

"What can this be?" she said.

Lucy looked at the package.
She saw something on it.
It said,

To Terry.
Happy Birthday!

"Oh!" said Lucy.
"The package is for Terry's birthday.
Now who is Terry?"

Lucy asked a policeman
on Green Street.
He didn't know Terry.

Lucy knew that twins lived
in the white house with red on it.
She knew that the last house
on the street had no children in it.
She knew that Betsy lived
in the big house with the fish pool.
She knew that Ellen
was Betsy's friend.

Lucy knew all that.
She **didn't** know where
Ellen lived.
She didn't know Terry.

Who Is Terry?

Lucy ran to tell her mother
about the package.

"Look, Mother!" Lucy said.
"This package was on the street.
It is for Terry's birthday.
But who is Terry?
I asked the policeman,
but he didn't know."

Lucy's mother looked
at the birthday package.

"I don't know," she said.

"Is Terry one of the children
on this street?"

"Not one that I know," said Lucy.

"Terry may be a boy or a girl,"
said her mother.

"We must try to find Terry."

"Where can we look for Terry?"
asked Lucy.

"You could try at the houses on Green Street," said Lucy's mother. "The package was on this street, so she may live on it."

"She?" asked Lucy. "Terry may be a boy."

Her mother laughed. "That's right," she said. "Terry may be a he or a she. See if you can find Terry in a house on this street. You may find the one where Terry lives."

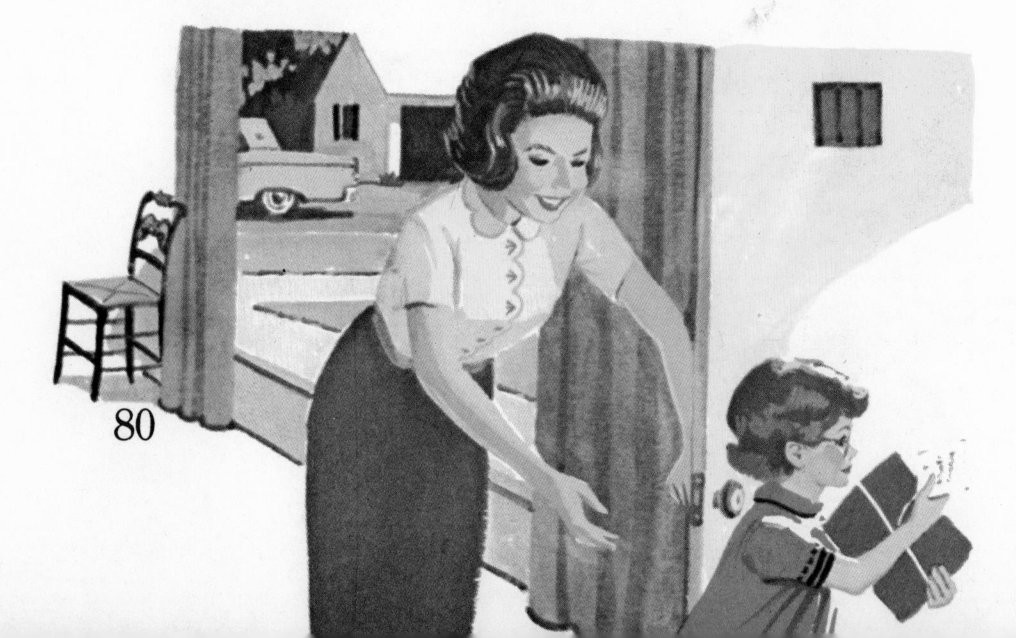

First Lucy took the package to the twins' house.

She saw Jack and Jim.

Lucy asked if they knew a boy or girl called Terry.

Both twins said together, "No, not a boy or a girl."

Lucy went on down the street.

She came to Betsy's house next.

She saw Betsy's little sister, Star.

Star didn't know a boy or girl called Terry.

Lucy went to the last house.
A little old man was there.
Lucy asked him if he knew
a boy or girl called Terry.

"A boy called Terry?"
asked the little old man.
"Or a girl?"
Then the little old man said, "No.
I don't know a boy or a girl
with that name."

Lucy went to all the houses.
She didn't find Terry.

Lucy's mother said, "Did you ask at the big white house?"

"Yes, I did," said Lucy.
"I saw a little old man.
He didn't know Terry."

Mother said, "The big white house has a little house back of it.
Did you try there?"

"I didn't know about that house," said Lucy.
"Terry may be there."

A New Friend

Lucy ran down the street looking for the little house.

As she came to the little house, she saw a big brown dog by it

The dog ran to Lucy.

"Hello!" said Lucy.

The dog began to jump up and down.

He jumped up on Lucy and tried to take the package.

"Why, he wants Terry's package!"
said Lucy.

She put the package up high
so the dog couldn't get it.
The big brown dog
jumped up high.
He jumped as high as he could.

Lucy put the package back of her.
That didn't help.
The dog ran around
and jumped for it.
Lucy tried hard to make him stop,
but she couldn't do it.

Just then a girl came out
of the little house.

Lucy knew the girl's name.

It was Ellen.

Lucy had seen Ellen with Betsy,
and she wanted her for a friend.

"Hello, Ellen," said Lucy.

"I didn't know you lived
on Green Street."

"Yes, I do," said Ellen.

"Where do you live?"

"In the new house," said Lucy.

"Good!" said Ellen.

"We can play together and be friends."

Then Ellen said to the dog, "Terry! Don't jump on Lucy!

She has on her good dress, and you may hurt her.

Don't be a bad dog!"

"Oh!" said Lucy.

"Is your dog called Terry?"

"Yes, that's his name," said Ellen.

"This is his birthday."

Terry's Birthday Package

"This package must be for your dog," said Lucy.

"It was on the street."

Ellen took the blue package.

Terry jumped high to get it, but he couldn't.

Ellen said, "Stop! I will give you your birthday package!"

As soon as Ellen put it down, Terry got into the package in a hurry.

Two things were in the package.
Terry looked at just one thing.
What he saw was a big bone.

How Terry went for that bone!

"That must be the best bone
Terry ever had," said Lucy.
"It is as good as a birthday cake
to him."

Ellen said, "It is a good thing
that you saw the package, Lucy.
Now I know where you live.
My little sister and I
can play with you.
I will take you to see
my friend Betsy and the Jones twins."

"Good!" said Lucy.

"Betsy has a fish pool,"
said Ellen.
"The twins have the cutest
little puppy you have ever seen.
You will just love that puppy!"

Terry looked up at the two girls.
Lucy said, "Happy birthday!"

Terry couldn't say "Thank you!"
He just said, "Woof! Woof!
Woof! Woof! Woof!"

Lucy laughed.
"Terry is the dog I love!"
she said.
"We don't have to bake
a birthday cake for him.
We can just give him a bone!"

My Zipper Suit

(*To be read to the children*)

My zipper suit is bunny-brown—
The top zips up, the legs zip down.
I wear it every day.
My Daddy brought it out from town—
Zip it up, and zip it down,
And hurry out to play!

Marie Louise Allen

Can You Say It?

A boy who was not at all big
Had fun with his little white p_ _.
Said the pig to the boy,
"I am not just a t_ _.
Look here and see how I can d_ _."

Friends on the Farm

Tommy and Ben

Tommy lived on a farm.
He had a big brother.
His brother's name was Ben.

One morning Ben ran into the house.

"Mother! Mother!" he yelled.

"The black and white cow has twins.

One of the twins is little
and one is big.

Daddy said I could have
the big twin for my calf!"

Tommy looked at his mother.
"I want a twin, too," he said.

"You are too little," said Ben.
"You have to be big like me
to take care of a calf.
I will take good care of my calf.
I will show him at the fair.
You are not big enough
to do that."

Tommy yelled, "I am too
big enough!"

He ran by Ben.

He ran on to the barn
where the cows were.

As he ran, he yelled back at Ben,
"I don't care what you say!

I am too big enough
to have a twin!"

Ben's mother said, "Don't quarrel
with your little brother, Ben.

Don't make him cry."

"Oh, Tommy won't cry," said Ben.

"He is not a baby."

Father Says No

Tommy went into the barn.
The mother cow was there.
Both her twins were with her.
The little twin looked like the big twin.
It was just little.

Tommy loved the little twin right away.
He wanted her for his own calf.

Tommy asked, "Daddy, may I have the little twin for my own?

May I show her at the fair?"

His father said, "No, Tommy.

You are not big enough to take care of a calf.

You are not old enough to show a calf at the fair.

You can have a calf to show when you are as old as Ben is now."

That was not what Tommy wanted.

He wanted the little twin.

Ben took good care of his calf.

When Ben went to the barn,
Tommy went, too.

He looked to see what Ben did
for his calf.

Then Tommy did it
for the little twin.

He did just what he had seen
Ben do.

"If this calf can't be my own,
I can take care of her," said Tommy.

"I love this little calf.

I will take care of her
just for fun."

Tommy took very good care
of the little calf.

It was a very good thing
that he did take good care of her, too.

You will find out why.

Tommy and the Little Twin

One day Tommy had something
for the little calf to eat.

She ran at it so hard
that Tommy fell over.

It hurt, but Tommy didn't cry.

Ben laughed at Tommy.

"I told you so!" he said.

"You can't take care of a calf.
You are not old enough.
You have to be big like me
to take care of a calf."

Tommy was mad.
He was very mad.
He yelled, "I can too
take care of my twin!
I am not too little!"

After that Tommy tried hard
not to fall when the calf ran at him.

Day after day Tommy took care of the little twin.

He loved her more and more.

The little twin began to love Tommy, too.

More and more she did what he wanted her to do.

Tommy called the little calf My Twin.

How he wanted her to be his very own!

One day Ben took his calf
out of the barn to let her run.

Tommy took his calf out, too.

When he tried to take her back
into the barn, she ran right by it.

She ran so hard
that Tommy fell down.

He just couldn't hold her.

Tommy tried hard.

But his father had to help
get the calf back into the barn.

Ben said, "I told you so!

You are not old enough
to hold a calf."

Now Tommy was mad again.
He yelled, "I am too old enough!
I take very good care of My Twin!
I will hold her from now on!
You will see!"

Ben said, "She is not your twin.
Dad didn't give her to you."

"That's her name," yelled Tommy.
"I call her My Twin."

After that,
Tommy did hold his calf.

Day after day Ben did things for Big Twin.

One day he said to Tommy, "Look how high my calf is.

I will make him a big calf and make him look good.

My calf will get a prize at the fair.

He will be the best calf there.

You will see!"

How Tommy wanted to take the little twin to the fair!

Tommy just knew the little twin could get a prize there.

If he could just take her to the fair!

Tommy knew he couldn't do that.

A boy had to be as old as Ben to show a calf at the fair.

Ready for the Fair

On the day of the fair,
Ben got up as soon as it was light.
After he had something to eat
he ran to the barn.
He had to get his calf ready
for the fair.

Tommy wanted to sleep,
but he got up as soon as Ben did.
He went with Ben to the barn.

The boys looked in the barn.
Ben's calf was not there!

The two boys told their father that Big Twin was not in the barn.

Their father and Ben went to find the calf.

They didn't let Tommy go.

Tommy said to the little twin, "You can't go to the fair.

But I will get you ready.

I will try hard to make you look good.

I want you to look as good as the best calf at the fair."

He got the little twin ready, as if she could go, too.

Soon a big truck came to the barn.
A man jumped out of the truck.

"Hello, friend!" he said to Tommy.
"Is your calf ready to go?"

He saw that the calf was ready.
He put her right into the truck.
He didn't let Tommy say a thing.

"Jump up here by me," he said.
"You can ride with your calf."

"Let me ask Mother," said Tommy.

Tommy called, "Mother, may I ride in the truck to the fair?"

His mother didn't know
that Ben's calf was out.
She didn't know
that his father and Ben were not there.

"Yes," she said.
"You may ride in the truck."

Tommy got
into the big, high truck with the man.
Off they went to the fair.

At the Fair

When they got to the fair,
the man in the truck said, "Come on!
Hurry! Take your calf out.
I must go get two more.
I must get them here for the show."

Then the truck man called
to a man with a big black book.
"Here is the calf
from the Whites' farm," he said.

The man with the book asked, "Is your name White?"

Tommy said, "Yes, but I am Tom—"

The man didn't let Tommy go on talking.

"Put your calf over there," he told Tommy.

He began to write something in his book.

Tommy put the little twin where the man said.

Tommy saw the people
looking around at the fair.
They were looking
at all the things there.
They looked at the cows.

One man was looking
at the little twin.
"I like the looks
of that little calf," he said.
"She will make a good cow."

Tommy liked that!

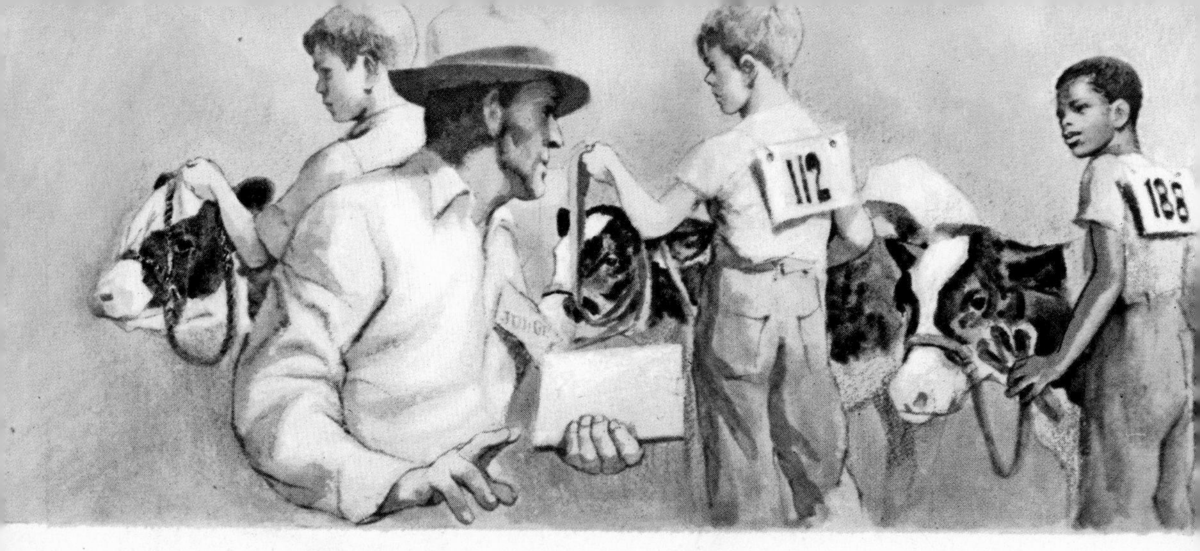

The man with the book
yelled out something.
Tommy didn't know what he said.

The boy next to Tommy
took his calf to the man with the book.
Then the next boy took his calf
over to the man.

All of them did that.
All but Tommy.
He didn't know what to do.
He knew the little twin
was not the right twin.
He knew he was not Ben.

The man began to count,
"One, two, three, four, five, six."
Then he looked at his book.

"There is one more calf," he said.
"I have not seen the calf
from the White farm.
Where is it?"

Then he saw Tommy and said,
"Come on with your calf, boy."

Tommy took the little twin over
with the others.

Each boy took his calf
around the man with the book.

Then the man said, "Stop!"

One calf didn't stop.

He ran away.

Two or three jumped
and ran around.

The boys couldn't hold them.

The man said, "Take them away!"

The little twin didn't jump
or run around.

She did just what Tommy
wanted her to do.

Each boy took his calf
around the man again and again.
Tommy saw the man look hard
at each calf and write in his black book.

Then the man came over
to the little twin.
He had something that said
First Prize.

All the people were looking
at the man.
They looked at Tommy
and his calf, too.

The man asked,
"Is this your own calf?"

"No, it is Daddy's," said Tommy.
"I am not Ben.
I am Tommy.
I am not old enough
to show a calf at the fair.
Ben has the other twin.
His calf was to come to the fair,
but it got away."

“Too bad!” said the man.
“You and this calf
make a good show together.
The calf is little,
but she will make a good cow.
We wanted her to have first prize.
We can’t give it to her
if she is not the right calf.
The prize must go
to this boy over here.”

Then the man said, “Tommy,
come back when you are old enough.
You will get the prize then
if you have the best calf.”

Just then Tommy's father came up.

"We did find Ben's calf," he said.

"We just couldn't get it here for the show."

Then he said to Tommy, "That is your calf from now on.

You took care of it.

You are big enough to have a calf of your own."

"Oh, thank you!" said Tommy.

"My Twin is the one thing I wanted!

Now she is my very own!"

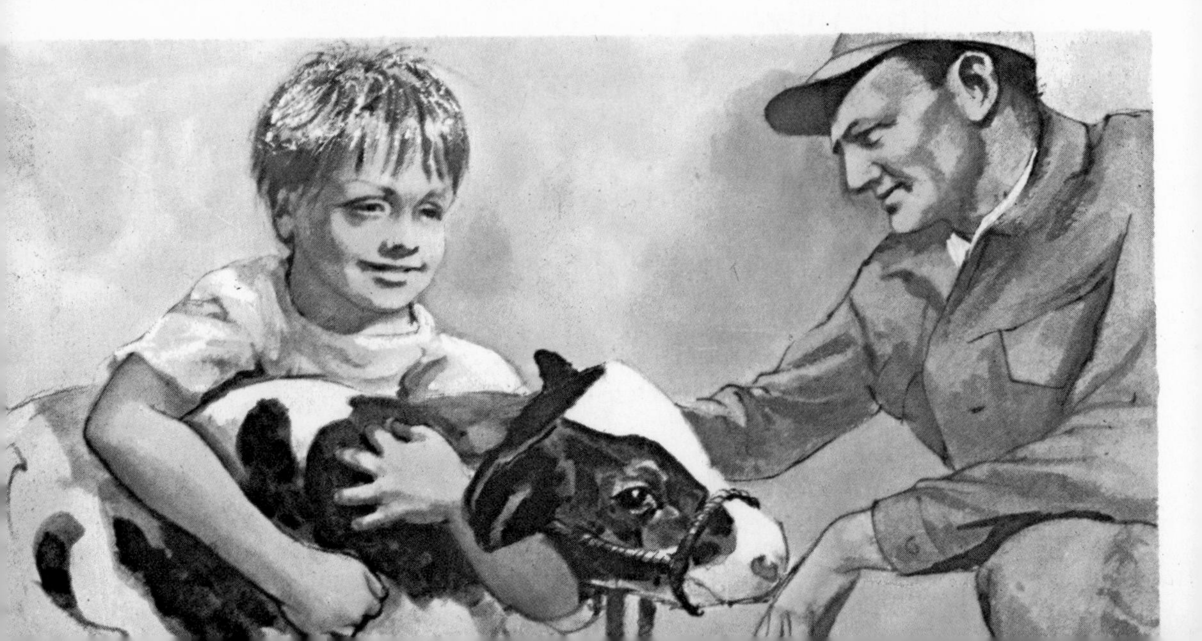

Teddy and Babs

Teddy was a little boy
who lived in a big, high house.
It was an apartment house.

Other people lived
in that apartment house, too.
But they didn't live with Teddy.
He lived with his little sister, Babs,
and his mother and father.
They all lived together
in one apartment.
Other people lived
in the other apartments.

Teddy and Babs didn't have a pet.
They both wanted one.
Both of them wanted a dog
for a pet.
Each of them said,
"A dog is the best pet for us."

Teddy asked,
"Dad, will we ever get a dog?"

His father said, "We can't have
a dog in this apartment.
If we ever live on a farm,
you may have one."

"It will be a big dog,
won't it, Dad?" asked Teddy.

Babs said, "Oh, no, Daddy!
I don't want an old dog.
It will be a little dog
that I can hold."

"You make me mad!" said Teddy.
"I won't have a little dog!"

"Don't quarrel," said their father.
"We will see about the dog
when we live on a farm."

Father's News

One day their father came home from work looking very happy.

"Get your things ready!" he said. "We are going to the farm."

"Oh!" yelled Teddy and Babs. "Will we live on the farm?"

"Yes, we will," said their father.

"What about your work, Dad?" asked Teddy.

His father said, "I will come here to work each morning.

Then I will go back to the farm at night."

"Who will do the work on the farm?" asked Teddy.

His father said,
"A farmer will work it for us.

He lives on the next farm.

He will take care of the cow, too.

You and Babs can help him."

"Oh, is there a cow?" asked Babs.

Her father said, "Yes,
and a little calf and goats.
There is an old barn, too.
You can play in it."

"Is there a dog on the farm?"
asked Teddy.

"Now," said his father.
"That's one thing
I didn't ask about."

Soon they all went to live
in their new home.
They took their things
in a big red truck.
When they got there,
a big dog ran out of the house.

"Oh, look!" yelled Teddy.
"That dog is just what I wanted!"

Babs was not happy.
The dog was so big he scared her.
She knew that he was Teddy's dog.
She did so want a little dog!

Just then Babs saw a little puppy!
It was just the right puppy for her.
She loved it right away.

The puppy ran right to Babs.
She took him up to hold him.

"My little puppy!" she said.
"My own little puppy!
You are the cutest little dog!
Teddy can have that other one."

New Friends

Babs and Teddy had fun
at their new home.
They liked to run and play
with their dogs.
They liked to help the farmer
work on the farm.

They could help him take care
of the cow and calf and horse.
They could help him with the goats.
They could do other things.

They had new friends there, too.

The farmer had two children, a girl and a boy.

The boy's name was Peter, and the girl's name was Jane.

Peter came to see Teddy each day.

He was the best friend Teddy ever had.

One day Teddy said,
"I will tell you what!
Let's play cowboys.
This will be my horse."

"Yes, let's do that," said Peter.

"I will be a cowboy," said Babs.

"You can't be a cowboy," said Teddy.
"Girls can't be cowboys."

"I don't have on a dress,"
said Babs.
"I can try to be a cowboy.
I have seen girl cowboys in books."

"I will ask Peter about it,"
said Teddy.
"How about it, Peter?"

Peter looked at Babs.

"We are looking
for a horse thief," he said.

"Can you catch a horse thief?"

"Yes," said Babs.

"Will you be scared?" asked Peter.

"No," said Babs.

Peter said, "All right,
but if you get scared, you can't play."

"What are you playing?"
asked Jane.

"We are not playing," said Peter.
"We are cowboys.
We are after a horse thief.
A thief got a horse
from the barn last night."

"Not one of Daddy's horses?"
asked Jane.

"No," said Peter.
"The horse thief is
just make-believe."

"Oh!" said Jane.
"We must catch that thief!"

"That's right!" said Peter.
"Let's find him!
To horse, boys!" he yelled.

Each of the children
got on a make-believe horse.
They went after
the make-believe thief.
They didn't catch the thief,
but they had fun.

A Night in the Barn

"I know what let's do,"
said Peter.

"Let's sleep in the barn all night.
If the horse thief came
in the night, we could catch him."

"That's right!" said Teddy.
"If we sleep in the barn,
we can catch him."

"Yes, let's sleep in the barn,"
said Jane and Babs.

Peter said, "You can't do it, Babs.
You will get scared if you do."

"No, I won't!" said Babs.

"Yes, you will," said Peter.
"You will get scared and cry."

"I won't get scared!" said Babs.
"I want to sleep in the barn."
She began to cry.

"Oh, all right," said Peter.
"But if you get scared,
you can't be a cowboy."

Peter and Jane ran home to ask
if they could sleep in the barn.
Teddy and Babs talked
to their mother and father about it.
The mothers and fathers said
the children could sleep there.

That night the four children went
to make up their beds in the barn.
They took the two dogs with them.
They soon had their beds ready.

At first they talked
and laughed together.
Then one by one they went to sleep.

That night something out
by the barn said, "Who! Who! Who!"

Teddy heard it.
He sat up in bed.

Again he heard it say,
"Who! Who! Who!"

Teddy was scared.
He wanted to be back
in his own little bed.

"Who! Who! Who!"
the noise came again.

Teddy got up and went out
of the barn.
He ran to the house
and got into his own bed.
It felt so good!

"My bed is the best bed of all,"
said Teddy, as he went back to sleep.

Soon Jane heard a noise.
She sat up in bed.
The noise was in the barn.
Jane looked all around,
but she couldn't find out what it was.

Then she heard the noise again.
Jane was scared!
She ran out of the barn.
She ran back to her house.
She got into her own bed.
It felt so good!

Soon she went back to sleep.

It began to rain.
Peter heard it and sat up.
He didn't know what the noise was, but he didn't like it.
It scared him.
He wanted to be at home.

Peter got up and went out.
He got very wet in the rain as he ran home.
When he got there, he took off his wet things.
Then he got into his own bed.
It felt so good!
It was the best bed he ever had!

Is Babs Scared?

The moon was down,
and the night was black.
Now Babs heard something.
She sat up in bed.

Babs said, "Teddy! What is that?"
She heard no one.

She called, "Peter! Jane!"
Again she heard no one.

Babs looked around and saw
that the other children were not there.

Babs began to get scared,
but she didn't cry.

Just then she felt something.
She looked down.
There was her little dog by her.

Babs took the little dog up
to hold him.
He got up close to her.
He felt so good!

Both Babs and the little dog
went back to sleep close together.

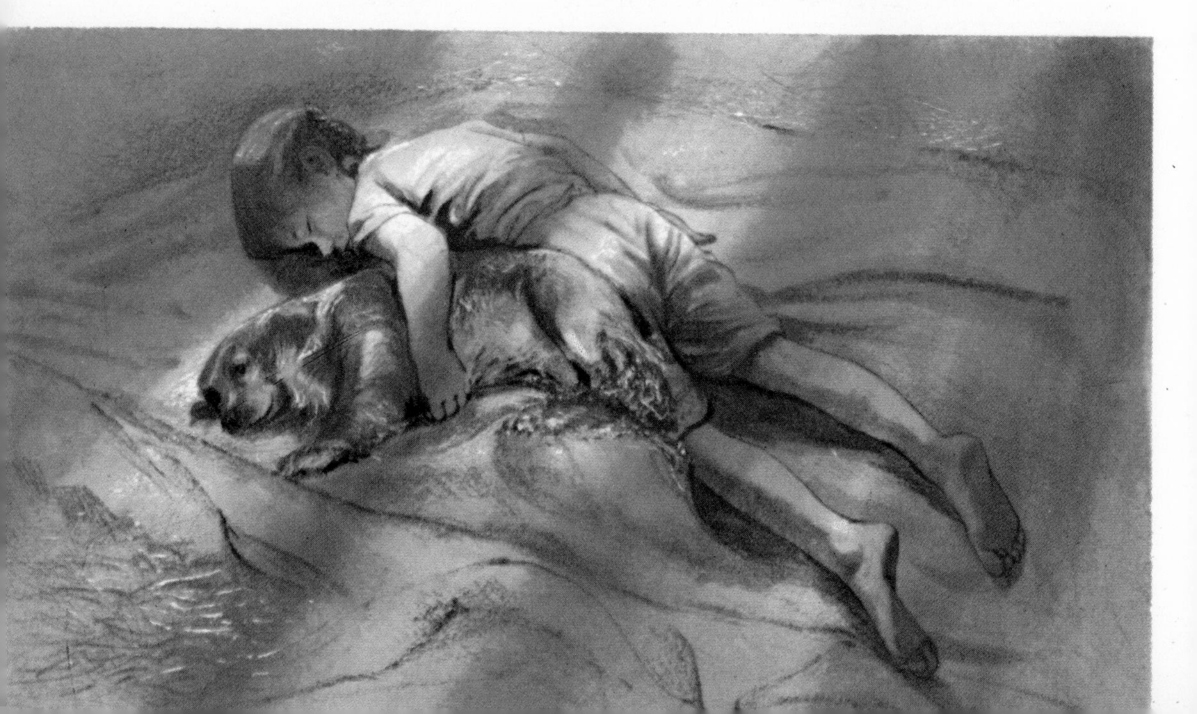

Morning came.
There was no more rain.
As soon as it was light,
Babs went back to the house.

"Oh, Babs!" said her mother.
"Were you scared?"

Babs said, "No, Mother.
I am a cowboy.
Cowboys are brave."

Horsemanship

(To be read to the children)

If you haven't got a pony,
    Like we haven't got,
An oak tree branch
    Has a very good trot.

It hasn't any tail,
    But it has a good bounce,
And it stands very still
    When a man dismounts.

Marchette Chute

With Horse and Dog

I will be a cowboy
    And ride, ride, ride.
I will have my little dog
    Close by my s_ _ _.
My horse will take me
    On and on
To ride all the day,
But when I want
    To go back home,
He will know the w_ _.

Fun with Make-Believe

The High Jump

A little brown rabbit lived with his mother.

They lived in a little home in the grass.

One day he said, "Mother!

I have no friends close by to play with me.

Please tell me a story about a make-believe rabbit.

Let him be a brave little rabbit."

"I will," said his mother.

Then Mother Rabbit said,
"A little rabbit lived with his mother.
He was a brave little rabbit."

"Just like me,"
said the little brown rabbit.

"That little rabbit wanted
to jump high," said Mother Rabbit.
"He wanted to jump over a mountain.
He wanted to jump that high."

"Just like me,"
said the baby rabbit.
"A make-believe rabbit like me!"

"Now one morning the wind came," said his mother.

"Did it rain?" asked the little rabbit.

"No," said his mother.
"It didn't rain.
The wind just blew and blew.
It blew very hard.
The little rabbit jumped high.
The wind blew him right over the mountain!
Then down, down he came."

The little brown rabbit
got very close to his mother.

"It was all right," said his mother.
"That little rabbit didn't fall hard.
A little green tree
didn't let him fall hard."

"Oh," said the little brown rabbit.
"He didn't fall hard!"

Now the little brown rabbit
felt brave again.

Mother Rabbit said, "The rabbit fell from the tree to the grass.

The fall didn't hurt him.

He liked the green grass, and he began to eat it."

"Just like me," said the little brown rabbit.

"Mother, is this story about me?"

"Oh, no," said his mother.

"It is not about you."

Over the Mountain

Then Mother Rabbit went on.
She said, "That little rabbit
heard a noise."

"Oh," said the little brown rabbit.
"A noise!"
He got up close to his mother.

"It was just the wind,"
said his mother.
"The wind blew the grass.
That is what he heard."

"Oh," said the little brown rabbit.
"The noise was just the wind
in the grass."

"So that little rabbit went on,"
said his mother.
"He went on and on.
He had fun all day."

"Then that little rabbit said, 'I must go home now.

I will jump back over the big, high mountain.'

"He jumped very high, but the wind blew him back.

He jumped again and again.

Again and again the wind blew him back.

He couldn't jump over the mountain."

"That little rabbit couldn't
get back home!" said Mother Rabbit.

The little brown rabbit
got very close to his mother.
"Mother," he asked.
"What did the little rabbit do then?'

His mother said, "Oh!
That little rabbit did
the right thing."

"Just like me!" said the little one.
Now he felt very brave again.

His mother went on with the story.

"That little rabbit couldn't
jump over the mountain.

So he went around it.

He went on and on,
and he went around the mountain.

At last he got home
to his mother."

"Just like me," said the little one.

"For here I am!"

His mother went on with the story.

"At last that little rabbit
did find his home again.

His mother was so happy
to see him!

She loved her baby rabbit."

"Just like you?"
asked the little rabbit.

He looked up at his mother.

"Yes," said his mother.
"Just like me!"

Patches

Patches was a little kitten.
She was a yellow kitten
with white patches on her.
That is why she was called Patches.

Patches had three brothers
and three sisters.
All her sisters and brothers
liked to play together.
Patches didn't want to play
with them.
She just wanted to sit and look up
at the birds as they flew over her.

Day after day Mother Cat said,
"Why don't you ever play, Patches?"

"I don't want to play,"
said Patches.
"I like to look at the birds."

The other kittens
went on with their play.
Patches just sat and looked
at the birds.

One day Patches saw
a very big bird in the air.
She had not seen a bird like that.

The bird flew over Patches.
She began to run after it.
With a jump and a bounce,
she ran as hard as she could.

Mother Cat saw her kitten
run after the airplane.

"What a kitten!" she said.
"Patches is trying to catch
an airplane!"

Patches didn't catch the airplane.

After that, when an airplane flew over, Patches ran after it.

"One day I will catch one," said Patches.

All the other kittens laughed at her.

Each day they asked her, "Did you catch an airplane?"

Each day Patches said, "No, but I am trying to catch one."

Then they laughed at her again.

One day Patches ran after
a big blue airplane.

It came down on the grass
close to Patches' house.

Patches looked at the airplane.

At first she didn't know
what to do.

It looked so big!

But she was a brave little kitten.

She ran right over to it.

Patches jumped up on the airplane and looked into it.

No one was in the airplane.

She went right in.

Soon she heard a man say, "There! It works all right now."

The man came into the airplane and sat down in the seat.

He didn't see Patches.

The airplane began to make a big noise.

Then it took off into the air.

Patches jumped up on the seat close by the man.

Then he saw her there on the seat.

"My! My!" he said.

"Kitten, where did you come from?"

"Meow!" said Patches.

She looked as if she wanted to say, "This is fun!"

Home Again

At first the man looked as if he were mad at Patches.

Then he laughed and said, "All right, little friend.

I will take you back home.

I won't be mad at you.

You didn't know what you were doing when you came in here."

The man said to the kitten,
"I will take you back now.
Come up here
where you can see something."
Then he put Patches
where she could look out.

The airplane flew high in the air.
Patches looked down.
First she saw streets
and apartment houses.
Then she saw trees and grass,
cows, horses, and goats.
Soon she saw a house,
a barn, and a little calf.

The house Patches saw
was the one where she lived.

The man saw it, too.

He took the airplane down again
close to the house.

"Now jump out, little kitten,"
he said.

"You have had enough fun."

"Meow!" said Patches.

She looked as if she wanted
to say, "Thanks for the ride."

Patches ran home.
She saw the other kittens playing together.
One brother asked,
"Did you catch an airplane?"

"Yes, I did," said Patches.
"That is what I was doing.
I went for a ride in it.
It flew high in the air."

Mother Cat looked hard at Patches.
She said, "Don't say that if it is not so!
Did you ride in an airplane?"

"Yes, I did, Mother," said Patches.

No one laughed now.
The other kittens
just looked at Patches.

Mother Cat said, "What do you know!
Patches did ride in an airplane!"

"She did!" said the other kittens.

One brother said,
"What a brave little kitten!
My own little sister is very brave!"

From that day on,
Patches ran after airplanes.
No one laughed at her now.

She didn't catch one again.
Patches didn't care.
It was fun to run after them
and try to catch them.

After all, she did catch one.
"I may catch one again,"
said Patches.

What's the Funniest Thing?

(*To be read to the children*)

What's the funniest thing you can think of?
What's the funniest thing you can think of?
    A monkey doing tricks?
    A house built out of sticks?
    An elephant juggling bricks?
What's the funniest thing **you** can think of?

What's the quietest thing you can think of?
What's the quietest thing you can think of?
    Grass growing?
    Snow snowing?
    A soft breeze blowing?
What's the quietest thing **you** can think of?

Beatrice Schenk de Regniers

Rockets Away!

Hap

Hap was a happy little boy.
That is why he was called Hap.
It was not his name.
At first people called him Happy.
Then they just said Hap.

Hap liked pets and play and people.
He liked boys and bikes and birds.
He liked trees and tricks and trucks.
He liked to fish.
The thing he liked best
was rockets.

He didn't have a rocket.
He had not seen one.
He **had** seen them on TV,
and he had a big book about rockets.

One day Hap said,
"Mother, I want to go to the moon.
I want to go in a rocket."

"Rockets! Rockets!"
said Hap's mother.
"You don't talk about anything
but rockets!"

Hap's father said, "If you go to the moon, what will you do? You can't walk on the moon."

"Why not?" asked Hap.

"You can't stay down on it," said his father.

"You will weigh very little on the moon.

You won't weigh enough to make you stay down on it."

"Oh," said Hap.

"My rocket book told me that.

I know that people
weigh very little on the moon.

Rocket men do something
about that.

The men put on something
to help them stay down on the moon.

Then they walk on the moon
in big, high jumps.

They jump like a rabbit,
but a rabbit can't jump as high.

It is a kind of rabbit walk."

Hap's mother laughed.

She said, "You don't have anything to put on to help you stay down. So you can't do that kind of walk."

"The rocket men could give me the right thing," said Hap.

His father said, "You are not old enough for that."

Hap said, "No, not now."

He felt bad.

He didn't know about the fun he was going to have at the fair.

At the Fair

The next day Hap and his mother and father went to the fair.

They went on the bus.

The busman said, "You will like the fair.

You can see just about anything there!"

Hap's mother wanted to see the cakes and other things that people bake.

His father wanted to go where he could see the new trucks.

His mother said, "You two go look at the things you like. We will get together again when we are ready to eat."

"All right," said Hap's father. "Hap can come with me."

Mother said, "Stay with Daddy, Hap, so you won't get hurt or lost."

Hap and his father looked first at the big red and yellow trucks. Then they walked around to see what other things they could see.

They saw many horses and cows.

They saw a cow and a calf
that Hap liked.

He said, "That's the cutest
little calf!"

They walked on and on and saw
many other things they both liked.

Hap liked all the things
that had wheels!

But he didn't get anything
with wheels.

He did get a balloon and a ball.

Hap Sees Something New

"Look, Daddy!" yelled Hap.
"See how that boy is walking!
Why does he walk like that?
How does he jump so high?"

"The pack on his back
makes him do it," said Hap's father.
"The pack has a kind of gas in it.
The gas is very light.
It helps the boy to jump high."

"What kind of gas is it?" asked Hap.

His father said,
"It is called helium."

"Does my little balloon
have helium in it?" asked Hap.

"No," said his father.
"Your balloon has air in it.
Air is a kind of gas, too.
It is not as light as helium.
The helium packs are very light.
They make the boy bounce high.
If he had on two of them,
they could hold him up in the air."

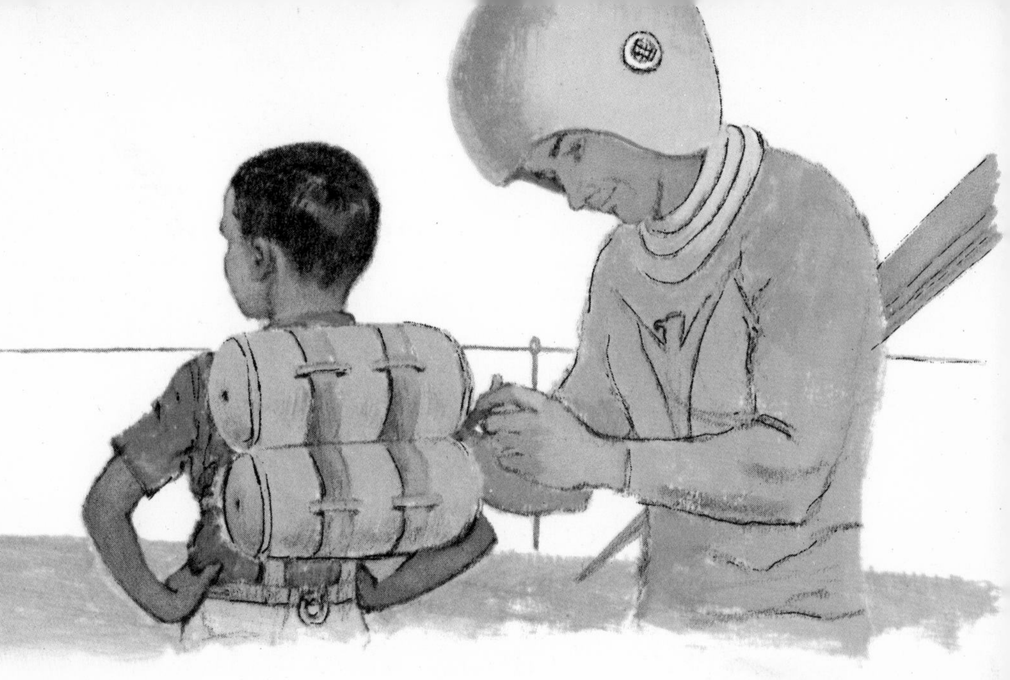

The man put two packs
on a big boy.

Then that boy bounced high
when he walked.

He bounced in big, high jumps.

It looked as if he were walking
on the moon!

"The busman on the bus was right!"
said Hap's father.

"One can see just about anything
at the fair."

"Hurry! Hurry!"
yelled the man with the helium packs.
"Try a walk on the moon.
Come one! Come all!
Come walk on air!"

Just then the man saw
Hap and his father.
"How about it, little man?"
he asked.
"Don't you want to walk
on the moon?"

"Oh, yes, I do!" said Hap.
"May I try it, Daddy?"

"Let me see about it first," said his father.

"I don't want you to float away."

"Oh, he can't do that," said the man. "He won't have enough helium packs to make him float away. This rope will hold him, too."

"Please, Daddy!" said Hap. "The rope will hold me."

"All right," said his father. "It looks like fun."

Hap's High Walk

"First I must find out
what you weigh," said the man.

"Then I will know how many packs
you must have.

Too many packs of this kind of gas
will make you float in the air.

The packs must be just right
to make you walk on the moon."

"What do I weigh?" asked Hap.

The man said, "You weigh
just enough for one helium pack."

The man put
one of the helium packs on Hap.
Hap began to float!
He floated up and up!

Hap came down,
then he bounced right up again.

"Let out the rope!" yelled Hap.
The man let out all the rope.
Hap went very high.
He went right over a little tree.

"This is fun!" yelled Hap.
"Look at me, Daddy!
I am walking on the moon!"

"I want your mother to see this," said his father.
"I will get her."
He went to get Hap's mother.

Hap walked back to the man.

Hap said, "That was fun!
Now I want to try
to float in the air.
Will more packs make me float?

"Yes," said the man.
"You will float if I give you
one more pack."

"Could I float away?" asked Hap.

"Oh, no," said the man.
"You can't float away.
This rope will hold you."

"Please let me try it," said Hap.

"All right," said the man.
He put one more pack on Hap.
Then Hap began to float.
He didn't bounce up high
and then come down again.
He just began to float
in the air.
He didn't come down at all.

"Look at me!" he yelled.
"I am floating!
Mother and Daddy, come and look!"

Just then the rope came in two!

Away went Hap.

He went over a little house.

He went up, and up, and up.

He went over the trees.

The man ran after Hap.

He tried to catch hold of the rope, but he couldn't.

"Come back! Come back!" he yelled.

Hap didn't come back.

He just floated on and on.

He was floating away when his mother and father came back.

"Oh! Oh!" yelled Hap's mother.
"Stop him! Stop him!
He is floating away!"
No one could stop Hap.

A man was working
on a very high pole.
Hap floated close to the pole.

His father called to the man
on the pole, "He is going close to you.
Try to cut the pack.
Cut the pack and let the helium out.
Then he will float down."

Hap floated close to the man on the pole, but not close enough.

The man couldn't cut the pack.

Hap floated away.

Then Hap floated back again.

This time he floated right up to the pole.

The man on the pole cut one of the packs!

All the helium went out of that pack.

Hap began to float down.

Hap floated down, down, down.

"Oh, Hap! Hap!"
called his mother.
"Don't ever do that again!
You scared me so!"

"No, Mother," said Hap.
"I won't.
I was scared, too.
I didn't want to float away."

Hap and the Rocket

Hap didn't have a sister.
He did have a big brother.
Hap's big brother didn't live
with him and his mother and father.
He was away at work.
He worked with rockets.

When Hap's brother came to see him,
he told Hap about his work.
He told about the many people
who were working together.
They were trying to make a rocket
to take a man around the earth.

"Will you go around the earth in the rocket?" asked Hap.

"No," said his brother. "My friend will go up in it. I help get it ready to blast off."

Hap knew "blast-off" was the time when the rocket first went into the air.

"Many others help to get it ready," said Hap's brother. "Each one of us must do good work. If just one does not do his best, the rocket may not work."

One day Hap asked,
"When will my brother come again?
I want to talk with him.
I want to know more about the man who is going around the earth."

"He can't come now," said Hap's mother.
"Here is a letter from him.
He wants us to go to see him.
The rocket will soon go up to take a man around the earth.
He wants you to see the blast-off."

That night Hap's mother showed his father the letter.

"Please, Daddy!" said Hap.
"Let's go!"

"What about school?"
asked his father.

"There will be no school that day," said Mother.
"School will be out for the holidays."

"That's right," said Hap's father.

"If we go on an airplane, we can get back before the holidays are over. I do want Hap to see the man go up in the rocket."

"That's what his brother wants, too," said Mother.

"I will write him that we will go."

Hap began jumping up and down and yelling, "Oh, boy! Oh, boy! I am going to see that rocket!" He ran to get his rocket book.

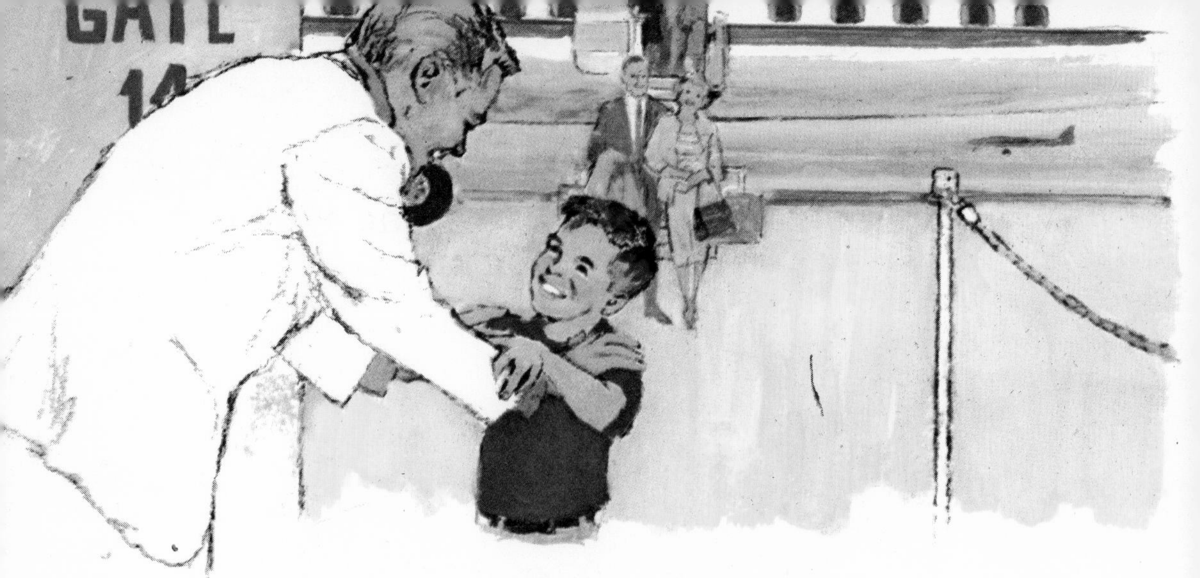

At the Blast-Off

Hap's brother came
to the airplane to get them.

As soon as Hap saw him he asked,
"When will the rocket blast off?

When will your friend go
around the earth?"

His brother said, "In the morning.

He will go around the earth then
if the weather is right."

"I want to see him go," said Hap.

Next morning Hap and his mother and father went out to see the rocket.

Many, many people were there to see it blast off.

The weather was right.

The rocket was ready.

Hap said, "The man in the rocket is called an astronaut.

If he does go around the earth, we will say that he orbits.

I saw that in my rocket book."

"Good for you!" said his father. "Now we want him to orbit!"

The countdown began.

Hap knew about the countdown, too.

A man counted to let the others know when to blast off.

The blast-off didn't come.

They had to stop the countdown before it was over.

Something was not right with the rocket.

The astronaut couldn't go up.

He couldn't orbit that day, after all.

Hap's brother felt very bad
about it.

"We are working hard," he said.

"We will get things right
with the rocket before we try again.
The astronaut will go up soon."

Hap asked, "Can we stay here?
Will we be here
when the rocket does go up?"

"You have just four more holidays,"
said his father.

"You must go back to school
when the holidays are over."

The men worked very hard
to get the rocket ready.
It had to be just right
before it could orbit the earth.
The astronaut could not go up
if the rocket was not right.

Day after day went by.
The school holidays were over,
and the rocket was not ready.
Hap and his mother and father
had to go back home.

Hap said, "I want to come back
when the rocket does go up."

They Try Again

One day Hap's brother called.
He said,
"We are ready to try again, Dad.
Can Hap come?"

Hap heard his father say, "No.
The rocket may not go up this time.
You may have to try again and again before it orbits.
The school holidays are over.
We can't take Hap out of school each time you try."

The next morning Hap got up to see the rocket on TV.

His father was right.

It didn't go up that day.

The rain came before it could go, and the weather was bad.

Again they had to stop the countdown.

Hap wanted to cry, but he didn't.

"When will the astronaut go around the earth?" Hap asked.

His father said, "I don't know, but they will try again."

The men did try again and again.
Each time they had to stop.
The weather was not right.

One day Hap's brother called again.
He said, "The rocket is ready, Dad, and the weather looks good.
The astronaut may go this time.
Please let Hap come for one day.
If the rocket does not go up this time, I won't ask again."

"I will go to Hap's school and ask about it," said his father.
He did, and they went that night!

The next morning Hap's father said,
"Get up, Hap!

The weather is right,
and the rocket may go up."

Hap and his mother and father
went out.

The big rocket was ready to go.

"Now it will orbit," said Hap.

His father said,
"It may not go up after all.

Something may not be right,
but we can't come back again."

"Yes, Daddy, I know," said Hap.
How he wanted that rocket to go!

The countdown began.
Hap heard the countdown
go on and on.
When it was over, he saw
a bright light and heard a big noise.
The blast-off had come.
The rocket was off!

Hap saw it go up, up, up.
The brave astronaut was off
to orbit the earth!

The rocket went so high
they couldn't see it.
They all went in to look at TV.

They saw people on TV
who were talking to the astronaut.
Hap heard the astronaut
talking to them from the rocket.

The astronaut said that things
were all right in the rocket.
He was all right, too.
The rocket was in orbit!
It was going around the earth.

Hap saw a boat on TV.

It was ready to get the astronaut when he came down.

The rocket went around and around the earth.

Then it began to come down.

Hap saw it on TV.

The astronaut was down!

He was all right!

He had orbited the earth!

Shooting Stars

(*To be read to the children*)

When stars get loosened
in their sockets,
They shoot off through the night
like rockets.
But though I stay
and watch their trip
And search where they
have seemed to slip,
I never yet have found a **chip**
to carry in my pockets.

Aileen Fisher

Word List for *LANDS OF PLEASURE*

The words introduced in LANDS OF PLEASURE, First Reader, are listed below in the order of their appearance. They are of three types:

Developmental (**boldface type**): Words which most pupils will not be able to identify independently. They are words that will be used in the development of word analysis skills, or words that should be taught as wholes because they are unsuited to analysis.

Skills Practice (regular type): Words which many pupils will be able to identify with the word-analysis skills that they have developed by that time, but for which other pupils will require more supervised skills practice.

Assumed (*italics*): Words which pupils are expected to identify independently with skills that have become well established.

For a complete description of categories, see the Teacher's Annotated Edition and Guide to accompany LANDS OF PLEASURE.

9.
10. **street**
houses
11. **live**
12. **Betsy**
sister
Star

---

13. **pool**
fish
Betsy's
boats
14. **was**
15. **white**
liked
16. **why**
her
mothers

---

17. **Ellen**
Linda
Ellen's
18. **dress**
black
Mother's
19. began
fell
called
20. **cry**
wet
21. **hurt**

---

22. **are**
23. **count**
by
24. **four**
five
six
25. **this**
26. got

---

27. yell
28.
29.
30. yelled
yelling
31. *jumping*
32. **were**
give
33.
34.

---

35. Jack
Jim
36. **brothers**
twin
37. **best**
together
brother

---

38. **morning**
twins
39. **sleep**
40. **write**
letter
41. **ever**
had

---

42. TV
looking
43. **puppy**
try
writes
44. **cutest**
seen

---

45. **care**
over
love
46. **next**
hard

---

47. **screen**
Jones
48. **prize**
49. **girl**
name
showed
prizes
50.
51.
52. **their**
names
53.
54. *girls*
played

---

55. *puppy's*
56.
57. **quarrel**
58. **Zip**
Snapper
59.
60.
61. came
62.

---

63. **could**
64. **whistle**
65. **both**
66. happy

---

67. **friends**
68.
69.
70. *counted*
letters
71. **last**
Zipper
. . . per
72. be

---

73. **Lucy**
lived
pets
sisters
74. knew
playing
75. **package**
friend
76. **birthday**
Terry
policeman
Terry's
77. where

78.
79. **find**
Lucy's
80. *lives*
81. took
82. **old**
there
83.

---

84. as
85. high
couldn't
86. *girl's*
87.

---

88. into
89. bone
things
thing
90.

91. **woof**

92.
93. am
pig

94.
95.
96. **Tommy**
Ben
brother's
97. **calf**
cow
98. **fair**
enough
99. barn
Ben's
cows

---

100. **own**
loved
says
101. when
102.
103. **very**

---

104. told
105. mad
106. **more**
107. hold
108. Dad
109.
110.

---

111. **ready**
112.
113. **truck**
114.

---

115. them
book
Whites'
116. **Tom**
talking
117. **people**
118.
119. others
120. **each**
121.
122. *Daddy's*
other
123.

124. *Tommy's*

---

125. **Teddy**
Babs
an
apartment
126. *apartments*
127.
128.

---

129. **work**
home
news
going
Father's
130.
131.
132. **scared**
Teddy's
133.

---

134. **horse**
135. **Peter**
Jane
136. *books*
137. **thief**
catch
138. **make-believe**
horses
139.

140.
141.
142. beds
talked
fathers
143. **heard**
sat
bed
144. **noise**
felt
145.
146. **rain**

147.
148. **close**
149. **brave**

150.
151.

152.

153.
154. **rabbit**
grass
155. **mountain**
156. **blew**
wind
157.
158.

159.
160.
161.
162.
163.
164.

---

165. **Patches**
kitten
166. *kittens*
167. **airplane**
air
trying
168.
169.
170. seat
works
171. meow

---

172. *doing*
173. *streets*
174.
175.
176.
177. *airplanes*

178.
179.

180.
181. *rockets*
182. Hap
183. *trucks*
184. **anything**
Hap's
185. **weigh**
stay
walk
186. men
kind
187.

---

188. *cakes*
189. *walked*

190. **balloon**
many

---

191. **gas**
does
pack
helps
walking
192. **helium**
packs
193. *bounced*
194.
195. float
rope

196.
197. *floated*
198.
199.
200. *floating*
201.
202. cut
pole
working
203. time
204.

---

205. **earth**
worked
206. **blast**
blast-off
207.
208. **holidays**
school
before
209.

---

210. **weather**
211. **astronaut**
orbit
orbits
212. *countdown*
213.
214.

215.
216.
217.
218.
219. bright
220.
221. *orbited*

222.